THE
# emoji puzzle challenge

THIS IS A SEVENOAKS BOOK

Published in 2017 by SevenOaks
An imprint of the Carlton Publishing Group
20 Mortimer Street
London W1T 3JW

A CIP catalogue for this book is available from the British Library.

Design: James Pople and Tokiko Morishima
Production: Yael Steinitz

ISBN 978-1-78177-766-4

Printed in Dubai

10 9 8 7 6 5 4 3 2 1

# THE emoji puzzle challenge

## MORE THAN 200 EMOJI ENIGMAS

Malcolm Croft

**SevenOaks**

# Contents

# Chapter 2: Stars of the Small Screen
··············

# Chapter 3: Emojis Go Pop!
··············

# Emoji Puzzles is Back!

In 2016, when the first *Emoji Puzzles* was published, emojis were everywhere. They formed 70 percent of every text message sent via phone; they were used in music videos, films and song titles. They had become our new friends, always there for us whenever we needed them to brighten our day. From Poop to Meh, LOL to OK, emojis always say what we need to say—and always make us laugh, too. Hours and hours have been spent sending our friends and family these tiny blobs of joy, so explicit in their meaning and yet so open to interpretation. And that's the pure beauty of emojis. Whether they express our true feelings, or help us disguise them, or even allow us to represent them in ways not quite yet understood, emojis help us communicate with each other. Plain and simple. In a frustrating world where everything is over-complicated for no reason whatsoever, it is emojis that make self-expression easy.

As Shakespeare said, "Brevity is the soul of wit." And you don't get much more brief than an emoji, do you? In one simple icon, you can suggest a multitude of meanings, emotions and ideas. Be honest, ever since emojis came on to the scene, you've never looked at an eggplant in the same way. And now,

that simple vegetable is sent billions of times every single week to people all over the world.

So, here we are a few years later and not much has changed. Emojis can still be seen around every corner, on every TV and phone screen. With the introduction of even more emojis planned for 2018, it's safe to assume that emojis are here to stay for a long time yet. Hopefully forever. Of course, one thing has changed. One big thing. In August 2017, the world got the emoji film it deserves. Called, aptly, *The Emoji Movie*, the film is a true blockbuster. The stars of our small screens have finally made the jump to the big screen with an all-star vocal and emoji cast.

Just because emojis are small, that doesn't mean they don't have big dreams. Where our favorite emojis will be in the future and what they'll be up to is anybody's guess. Who knows, an emoji may even be elected president one day. Stranger things have happened.

Anyway, enjoy even more emoji puzzles, and remember to use your emoji-nation as much as possible.

# Emojification!

**HOW THE PUZZLES WORK**

The emoji puzzles contained in this book are a mixed bag of ideas. You've got to use your emoji-nation to work them out. Some will be simpler than others; some may leave you scratching your head. Many puzzles are representations of the title of a film, song or TV show. Others are even more devious and describe the plot or throw in a few red herrings designed to confuse. Some emoji puzzles may even appear in the wrong place. After all, this is a puzzle book—the point is to make you think. But not too much!

These puzzles are great to impress your buddies—text them to see if they can work them out or even make up their own. There are easy, medium and difficult puzzles peppered throughout the pages, using different devices to deceive your brain. Let's quickly run through them ... just to make sure you're paying attention! Remember, some emojis can be open to interpretation!

**TITLE BASED**
Simply guess the title from the emojis in front of you.
Remember—they won't always be in the correct order.
Can you guess this one?

ANSWER: *The Lion King*

**EASY, RIGHT?**

## PLOT BASED

Guess the song, TV show or film from its narrative or its themes recreated in emojis. Can you work this one out?

ANSWER: *127 Hours*

## DEVIOUS

Some of the puzzles will be deliberately devious, such as this one.

ANSWER: *The Fifth Element*

## BONKERS

And some puzzles may just be plain outrageous!

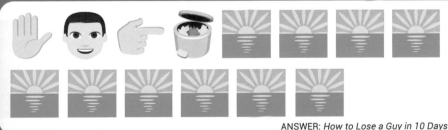

ANSWER: *How to Lose a Guy in 10 Days*

# 1

# Let's All Go to the Movies!

There's no better place to start an emoji puzzle adventure than at the movies. With every type of film genre covered, there's an emoji puzzle here for everyone.

Skip forward to your favorite type of film, or work through each one in order, it doesn't matter. When you complete the puzzles, then—and only then—can you move on to the next chapter.

No cheating!

# Name the Movie

........................................................

## ACTION

Bond. Bourne. Braveheart. Black Widow. The list of action and adventure heroes and heroines is endless. What greater way to pay homage to all of their stunts, skills, quips, and seductive one-liners than with an emoji puzzle or two? So, can you guess the titles of these action and adventure films?

**1**

**2**

**3**

**4**

**5**

**6**

**7**

# Name the Movie

......................................................

## CLASSIC

Classic movies are endlessly entertaining. You know the ones. The films that come out on a Sunday afternoon, or at Christmas, or anytime you get together with your family and don't want to talk to each other. From *Die Hard* to *Toy Story*, *Jumanji* to *The Shining*, anything can be a classic, but for this section we've chosen the true golden oldies of the silver screen ...

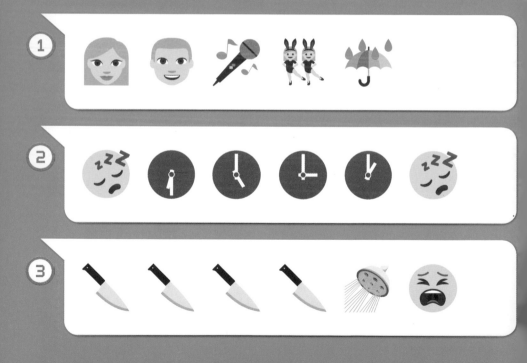

**4**

**5**

**6**

**7**

# Name the Movie

**ACTION COMEDY**

Comedy is one of the most popular genres at home and at the cinema. It's official—everybody loves to LOL! With the rise of home-streaming services such as Netflix and Amazon, there is now a plethora of awesome blockbuster movies that are also funny. But to throw a wrench into all this messing around, can you spot the odd show out?

**1**

**2**

**3**

**4**

**5**

**6**    2 0 4 9

**7**

# Name the Movie

.........................................................

## BLOCKBUSTER

In the 21st century, blockbuster movies are big business. With extra special effects, big budgets, huge stars, and massive expectations to recoup their costs, blockbusters are brilliant when you just want to turn your brain off and enjoy loud noises and awesome colors. When it comes to emoji puzzles, however, you need to turn your brain back on and employ your EQ—emoji-quotient.

**1**

**2**

**3**

**4**

**5**

**6**

**7**

# Name the Movie

**DISASTER**

Disaster films are the best. Especially when everyone dies except the dog, or the little kids. Whether it's a tsunami, a volcano, a string of earthquakes or even a meteor strike, there is always something about to eradicate humans from the face of the Earth. Thankfully, there's always an action hero and their trusty comedic sidekick, or a wily group of friends to save the day! Can YOU save the day, and help solve these simple puzzles?

**4**

**5**

**6**

**7**     END

# Name the Movie

**ANIMATED**

Animated movies, as well as live action movies, are conquering box offices all over the world. No longer just for kids, and not anchored down by reality, this popular genre of movie can straddle the entire spectrum of emotions, characters, and universes. These movies can personify rabbits, emotions, and inanimate objects. They can take place in your body, in outer space, or in your back garden. The possibilities are endless. Be thankful you only have seven to solve ...

**1**

**2**

**3**

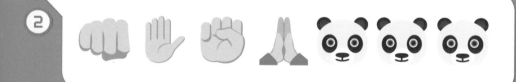

**4**

**5**

**6**

**7**

# Name the Movie

**SUPERHERO**

Iron Man. Superman. Batman. Spiderman. Wonder Woman. Thor. Hulk. Captain America. Dr. Strange. They've all saved the day more times than we can remember and we all owe them a debt of thanks. Now the most popular form of blockbuster, it feels like a new superhero film is released every week, and their heroes exist in many different shapes and sizes, on planet Earth and in outer space. Who's your favorite? Is it one of the guys or gals in these movies?

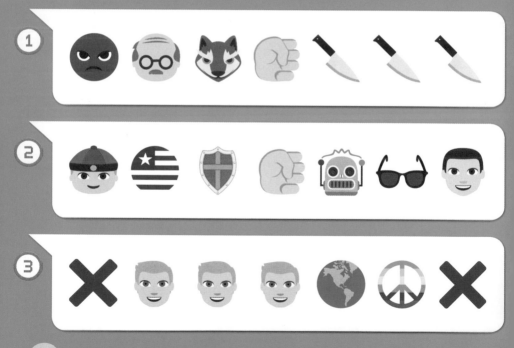

**4**

**5**

**6**

**7**

# Name the Movie

....................................................................

## MONSTER

Monster movies! Bugs, spiders, insects, lizards, killer monkeys, aliens, horrible bosses—monsters come in a multitude of guises. What is your favorite harbinger of doom, destroyer of worlds and evil incarnate? If you had to choose, which monster would you least like to see outside your front door? There is an odd monster out in these seven movies. Take a guess at which one it could be!

1

2

3

**4**

**5**

**6**

**7**

# Name the Movie

**SPORT**

Sporting films are always a great opportunity for serious A-list actors and actresses to show off their acting chops. Every one of the films listed below has an Oscar winner attached. From *Bull Durham* to *Tin Cup*, *A League of Their Own* to *The Phenom*, sports movies show us just how much hard work it is being a world-class athlete. Except for *Balls of Fury* or *Blades of Glory* ... they were just plain silly. To win an additional trophy, can you name the odd one out?

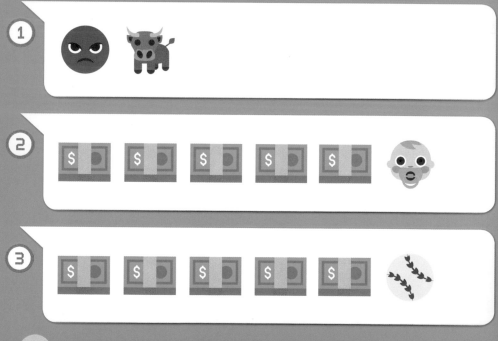

1

2

3

**4**

**5**

**6**

**7**

# Name the Movie

......................................................

**CRIME**

Crime movies, including gangster and heist, are always fun films to watch on a quiet evening in. The gruesome murders, the whodunnit plots, the duplictious backstabbing of best friends, the sleeping with the enemy, and the money. Bucketloads of money. What's not to like? But not all crime looks the same— so don't be surprised if one or more of these movies feels like it belongs somewhere else.

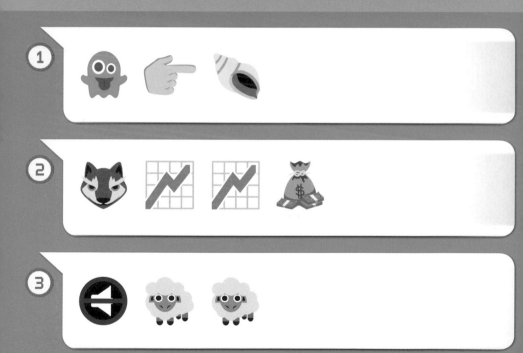

**1**

**2**

**3**

**4** 🔫🔫🔫🔫 😀 🔫🔫🔫🔫
🔫🔫🔫🔫 🔫🔫🔫🔫

**5** 😵 ‽‽‽‽‽‽ 🗺️ 💨 🚂
‽‽‽‽‽‽

**6** 😠😠😠😠😠😠😠😠

**7**

😁

# Name the Movie

...................................................................

**MASTERCLASS**

Every year the Academy Awards are predominantly focused on two gongs—Best Actor and Best Actress. Very rarely (never) do these awards go to actors for a comedic performance. It is usually for a serious role in a drama. These Oscar-worthy films are now acting classics. But can you guess the films?

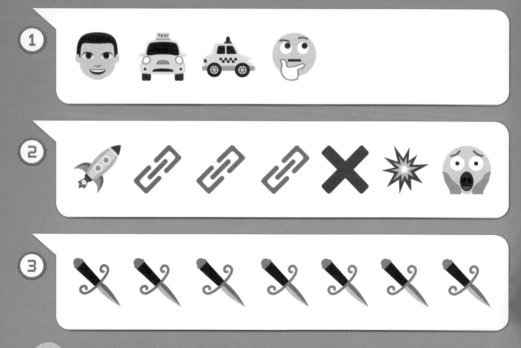

# Name the Movie

**SEQUELS**

Sequel, trilogy, tetralogy, pentalogy—whichever film comes out after the original is always, sometimes unfairly, compared to the first film. Many times the sequel outshines the original, but often it pales in comparison. We've thrown in a red herring—can you fish it out?

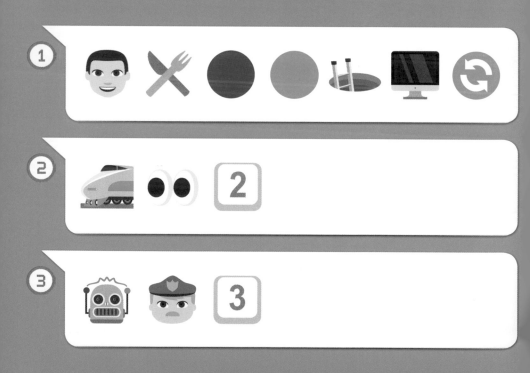

1

2

3

**4**

**5**

**6**

**7**

# Name the Movie

## HORROR

Any film that makes you look under your bed or check your wardrobe after you've watched it is a horror movie. These films have been made to scare the living daylights out of you, and the best way to do that is to manipulate your imagination. From terrifying witches, demons and creatures of unknown origins to psychopathic teachers, creeps and weirdos, there are 101 ways to die when you're at the hands of a raving lunatic. Cue evil laughter.

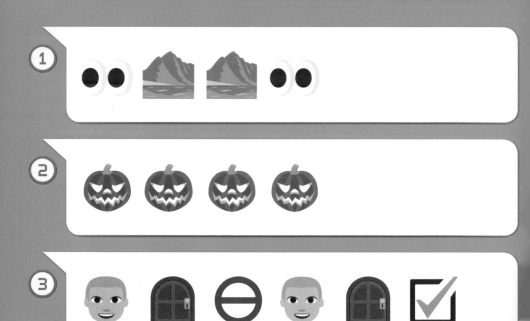

**4**

**5**

**6**

**7**

# Name the Movie

**ROMANTIC COMEDY**

Every movie has a squishy kissy part, even action movies when the tough hero gets the girl. Some movies, however, are all touchy-feely bits and these are called romance movies. The plots are usually paper thin (girl meets guy, guy meets girl, wires get crossed, etc.), but we fall for them every time. Since the dawn of Hollywood, romances and romcoms (romantic comedies) have been specially formulated to trick us in to crying like babies come the moment when the two star-crossed lovers touch tongues. Can you guess these lovesick emoji puzzles?

**1**

**2**

**3**

**4**

**5**

**6**

**7**

# Name the Movie

......................................................................

**SCIENCE FICTION**

From laser-beam blasts to setting phasers to stun, sci-fi flicks are stuffed with awesome tricks that make our eyes and ears shout WOW—even though no one in space can hear us scream! Every summer, our favorite directors bring us new sci-fi movies that make outer space look both beautiful and terrifying. But sci-fi films aren't all set a long time ago in a galaxy far, far away—many futuristic films can be set here on earth, too. Can you spot those ones?

# Name the Movie

Creatures straight from hell, monsters made from evil, demons possessed by doom, parents swapping bodies with their teenage children—we've all seen fantasy movies. But these films aren't all scruffy heroes wielding swords and casting spells—some fantasy movies can be only a smidge removed from reality. Can you identify both the epic and the freaky fantasies below?

**4**

**5**

**6**

**7**

# Name the Movie
..................................................

## MUSIC

From *Frozen* to *La La Land*, musicals are hugely popular. But animated and live action movies are often stuffed with songs, even if they're not musicals. Not all the movies on this page are musicals, per se, but music is a dominant feature that plays an important part in the narrative. So, with a "1, 2, 3, 4!" let's go ...

**1**

**2**

**3**

**4**

**5**

**6**

**7**

# Name the Movie

**THRILLER**

Expertly keeping your butt as close to the edge of your seat as possible, thrillers are filmmakers' ways of letting you know they are in control. They come in all shapes and sizes—from whodunnits to heists, and from gangster flicks to romcoms-gone-wrong. You'll have to guess which is which from the list. And to ensure you stay on the edge of your seat, we may have thrown in an unusual suspect to keep you guessing. Can you spot it from the line-up?

**1**

**2**

**3**

**4**

**5**

**6**

**7**

# Name the Movie

**OSCAR WINNERS**

Every February (or March) the world goes a little bit more nuts for A-List acting talent, when Oscar season rolls into town. Tongues wag, ears burn, and guts speculate as all eyes head towards Hollywood. Who will win? Who will lose? Who will look gracious in defeat? And who will have a mega meltdown on camera? These are some of the most recent Academy Award-winning movies across the various categories.

**1**

**2**

**3**

**4**

**5**

**6**

**7**

# Name the Star

Time to mix things up a little! Instead of simply naming the movie title—that's too easy—can you guess the movie title AND the film's leading man? To survive this round it'll require all of your EQ (emoji quotient) and film knowledge to unite in your brain. Don't worry, there isn't anything too demanding in here. Or is there?

**1**

**2**

**3**

**4**

**5**

**6**

**7**

# Name the Star

BEST ACTRESS

Despite massive gender inequality in Hollywood, the truth is that when it comes to making awesome movies, women rule the roost. Not all of these films have won Academy Awards, but thanks to the leading ladies who raised the game, these films have become classics of their genres. Guess the film, name the actress, and claim your prize as emoji master! Clue: we've chosen films you wouldn't normally expect ...

**1**

**2**

**3**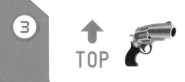

**4**

**5**

**6**

**7**

# Name the Star

........................................................

## BEST DIRECTOR

Movies are made by directors. Nobody really knows what they do or how they do it, but it's their job to shout "Action!" and "Cut!" and capture a story written down on paper. Without weird and wonderful directors, we'd all have to read books—boring! Can you guess the director? Can you name the movie? Do both, and you'll have earned the right to turn the page. Fail, and back to page one you go!

**4**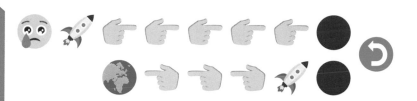

**5**

**6**

**7**

# 2

# Stars of the Small Screen

Watching TV is better than going to the movies these days. Why? Because thanks to streaming technology, we can access high caliber TV shows to bingewatch over and over again from the comfort of our own homes. Picture the scene: you're back from a hard day's work, or school, you're settling in front of the TV with the ones you love, and you're chilling with a show that has so many episodes you can watch it until the sun comes up. As always, emojis will be there by your side. Can you spot these stars of the small screen?

# Name the Show

••••••••••••••••••••••••••••••••••••••••••••••••••••••••••

**BEST OF BINGEWATCH**

Bingewatching has become the buzzword of the current tube-obsessed generation. Who can blame them when there is this much decent TV to be watched? At the click of a button, or the tickle of a mouse, we can get our daily fix of all the shows we love and bunker down for the night with our favorite TV characters. The programs below are all ridiculously bingewatchable—once you pop, you just cant stop!

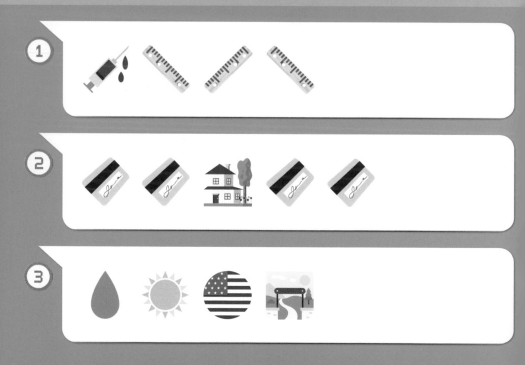

1

2

3

**4**

**5**

**6**

**7**

# Name the Show

## COMEDY

Comedies can come in all shapes and sizes. Some can make you laugh out loud, some make you titter quietly, some make you pee just a little bit, and some are worthy of only an eye roll. Anything that makes you smile deserves consideration in this section, so keep your emoji eyes peeled—these aren't your average comedy shows. There are too many good shows to choose from, but these are some of our favorites. Are they yours, too?

**1**

**2**

**3**

**4**

**5**

**6**

**7**

# Name the Show

## DRAMA

Dramas are a great excuse for actors and actresses to show off their acting chops, and make us engage with the story at home. In order to showcase the very best of drama, we've included different genres, just to keep you on your toes. Remember: emojis are open to interpretation, so you may have to do what Brad Pitt did in the film *Seven*—think outside the box!

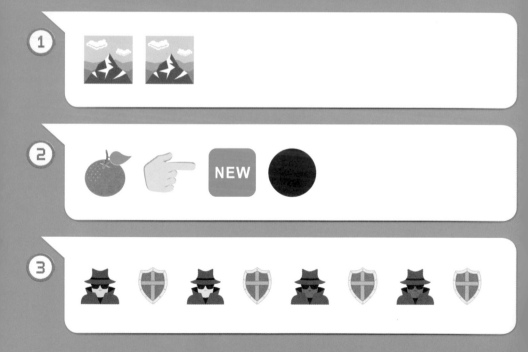

**4**

**5**

**6**

**7**

# Name the Show

••••••••••••••••••••••••••••••••••••••••••••••••••••••••

**EVEN MORE COMEDY**

Comedy is so much fun we thought we'd include it twice! Here, we've gone back in time and concentrated on the classic comedies of yesteryear, so these shows are no longer being made. For bonus points, can you name the year they first aired? Your emoji-telligence will be twice as brilliant if you can.

For those of you who are youngsters—anyone born in the 00s—feel free to skip this page!

**4**

**5**

**6**

**7**

# Name the Show

## ACTION AND CRIME

Action and crime TV shows are booming all around the world. From *Line of Duty* to *Luther*, *Sherlock* to *Elementary*, *Breaking Bad* to *Brooklyn Nine-Nine*, cops and robbers have always fascinated TV-watchers. The selection of puzzles below is a case you emoji detectives have to solve. But be warned—not every riddle is as straightforward as it seems!

**1**

**2**

**3**

**4**

**5**

**6**

**7**

# Name the Show

**FANTASY AND REALITY**

When fantasy and reality TV meet it is a thing of beauty to observe. Imagine *Keeping Up with the Starks*: a mash-up of *Keeping Up with the Kardashians* and *Game of Thrones*. How cool would that be? Alas, the day when those two shows unite will also be the day hell freezes over, and although winter may well be coming, I suspect we shall never see this program. Boo! However, to keep your appetites whetted, here is our very own mash-up of fantasy and reality shows. Can you guess which is which?

**1**

**2**

**3**

**4**

**5**

**6**

**7**

# Name the Show

................................................................

**SCIENCE FICTION**

A long time ago in a galaxy far, far away, some awesome person decided that the big-screen thrills of outer space needed to be seen in a more intimate setting, and thus sci-fi TV was born. Now, we have every type of adventure out in space. Science fiction isn't all about space, though: with futuristic apocalypses, alien encounters, awesome new technologies and shadow agencies up to no good, sci-fi is all around. This first one is particularly tricky ...

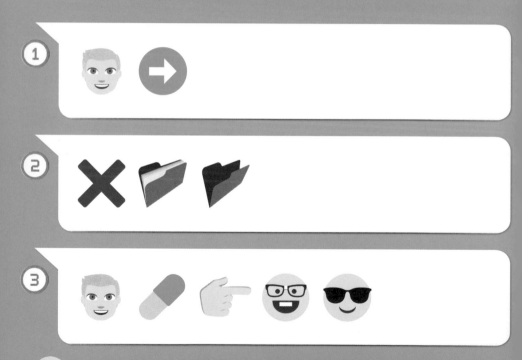

1

2

3

**4**

**5**

**6**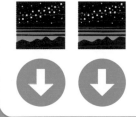

**7**

# Name the Show

**ANIMATED**

Animated TV shows these days are made for kids of all ages. Ever since *The Simpsons* first aired in 1989, all the rules about cartoons have been broken. There are now scores of inappropriate and hilarious cartoon characters who have become part of our own families. Below is a mixture of classic cartoons and modern animated shows, proving just how diverse the field can be.

**1**

**2**

**3**

**4**

**5**

**6**

**7**

# Name the Show

........................................................

## ROMANTIC DRAMA

When it comes to small-screen TV romances, there is nothing like a long drawn-out kiss, cuddle or dirty snuggle under the sheets to keep audiences glued to their sets. Ross and Rachel knew it. Chandler and Monica knew it. Joey and Phoebe should have known it. TV history is littered with romances that have swept us away to dreamy wonderland, and made us all believe in love at first sight, burning desire, and the power of that first kiss. But not all romcoms have happy endings ...

**1**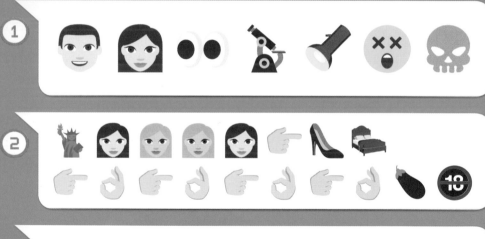

**2**

**3**

**4**

**5**

**6**

**7**

# Name the Show

**HEROES AND VILLAINS**

There's nothing like a good old-fashioned fist fight between good and evil. We love to see our heroes and heroines get into seemingly doomed scenarios only to escape without a moment to spare, using nothing but dogged determination. Emojis are lovers, not fighters, but there are a few emojis we can employ to denote a bout of fisticuffs. After all—without evil, how do we know true goodness?

**1**

**2**

**3**
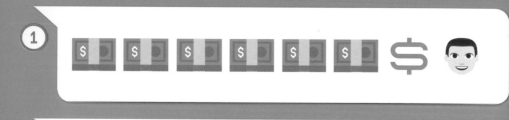

**4**

**5**

**6**

**7**

# Name the Show

**EPIC DRAMA**

HDTVs is awesome for sweeping epic dramas. The gush of blood, the cries of pain, the squeals of ecstasy, the swoon of lusty affection, and the groan of a zombie or two—they all look and sound great on TV. These days, epic TV dramas are just long enough to grab our attention and keep us hooked until the next episode. Keep your emoji-nation focused ... some of these will require your concentration.

**1**

**2**

**3**

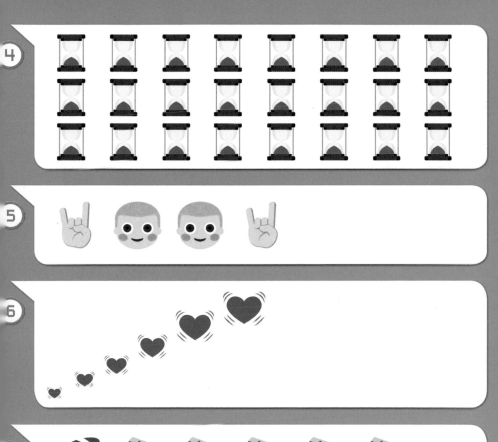

**4**

**5**

**6**

**7**

# Name the Show

## BEST OF BRITISH

When it comes to amazeballs television, nobody does it better than the British. What the island may lack in size, it more than delivers in wallops of epic and gut-wrenching drama and bone-shaking comedy. The envy of the world, British TV has more iconic characters and shows than anywhere else, a point proved by the fact that every other nation on earth keeps nicking them and making their own versions. Keep your wits about you, these emoji puzzles will put your knowledge to the test. Just kidding! They're easy ... right?

**1**

**2**

**3**

**4**

**5**

**6**

**7**

# Name the Show

**BEST OF THE USA**

Forget what was said on the previous page. When it comes to knockout TV, nobody does it better than the US. They have it all: multiple networks, tons of episodes, awesome actors, big budgets, brilliant ideas, and the energy to keep shows going for season after season after season without flagging. In fact, with so many amazing shows, it's hard to keep track of them all. It's even harder to watch them all. You'll be forgiven if some of these don't ring any bells, but give them a try anyway ...

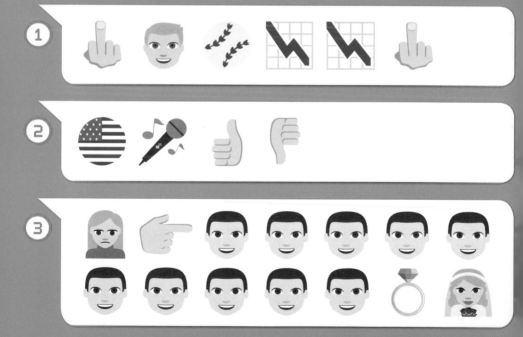

**4**

**5**

**6**

**7**

# Name the Show

**A LITTLE BIT OF EVERYTHING**

We're going to mix it up again just to keep things fresh. No genre. No clues.
You've got to rely on your pure emoji instincts to work these little critters out.
Think outside the emoji, and remember they are all open to interpretation. That
said, it's not rocket science! There's no cheating allowed, so if you get stuck—
tough! Answer pages are for wimps.

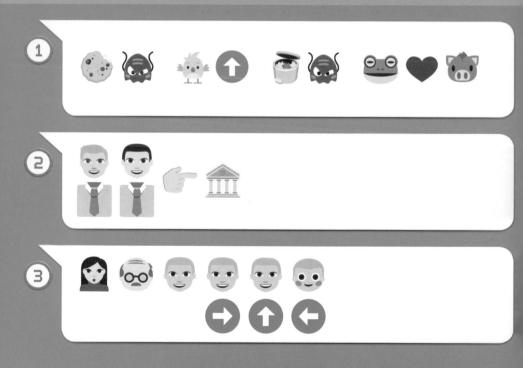

**4**

**5**

**6**

**7**

# Name the Show

**CLASSIC TV: UK**

Classic TV. You know what we mean. The kind of shows you watch over the Christmas holidays, when you're too stuffed full of food to move or change the channel. Not that you'd want to. When the TV is this darn brilliant, no one in the family is going anywhere. So, grab some snacks, pull up a comfortable chair, and get your sleuth on with these UK-TV classics ...

**1**

**2**

**3**
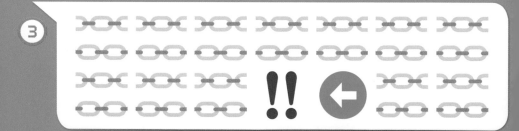

**4**

**5**

**6**

**7**

# Name the Show

**CLASSIC TV: USA**

Boundless emoji-nation. That is what is required for these puzzles. Some are straightforward, some will make you scratch your chin. Some are deliberately ambigious and some are beyond simple. The very best of US TV awaits you. These are the shows that remain at the top of bingewatch faves, even if some of them are more than a few decades old! Good TV never goes out of style, that's our motto.

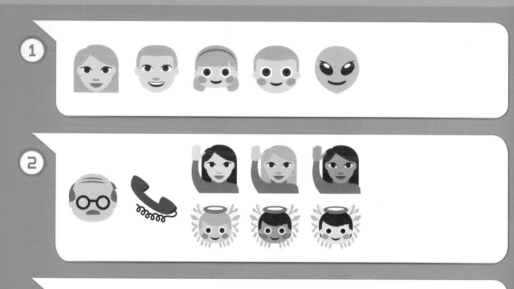

**4**

**5**

**6**

**7**

# Random

••••••••••••••••••••••••••••••••••••••••••••••••••

## ANYTHING GOES

Time to mix it up again. Just when you thought it was safe to go back in the water. This time we've stuffed a load of ideas in a bag and pulled them out one by one, in no particular order. TV shows, films, whatever, it's all here waiting to be put back together again. If there are shows here you have never seen, then put them on your bingewatch list, because they're awesome ...

**4**

**5**

**6**      BACK

**7**

# Random

**FILM AND SHOW**

It's often said these days that Hollywood hasn't had an original idea in decades. What with all the prequels, sequels, trilogies, reboots and reimaginings, it's easy to be cynical. That said, when the source movies and TV shows are as good as the emoji puzzles featured below, who cares? If it's a great movie it deserves to be watched over and over again on the small screen. How many of these have you seen? Extra points if you've watched both the TV and movie versions!

**1**

**2**

**3**

# 3

# Emojis

# Go Pop!

Emojis are well known for their love of all genres of music. They like to mosh, swing, dance, slide, and jump to the rhythm of the beat. For this final chapter, we've saved the best until last—because music is a big part of all our lives. In this modern world of streaming, Spotify, YouTube and Apple Music, music is now more accessible than ever before. So, we've got a lot to do! Press play and let your emoji-nation step in time!

# Name the Song

**POP**

Pop music and emojis are like bacon and eggs—they taste delicious together, especially if you throw on a bit of Salt-N-Pepa. There is a mixture of classic and modern pop puzzles to solve on this page, so you'll have to put your thinking caps on! Hopefully, once you've solved them, the songs will stay in your brain for the whole day.

**1**

**2**

**3**

**4**

**5**

**6**

**7**

# Name the Song

......................................................

**ADELE**

Ladies and gentleman, this artist requires no introduction, but we have to give her one because we need to fill this space. It's Adele. Making waves ever since her first album, *19*, this multi-award-winning songwriter and singer has dominated the world of pop more successfully than any other artist currently around. To date, Adele has sold more than 40 million albums and more than 50 million singles. That's bonkers! And not bad for a girl from Tottenham!

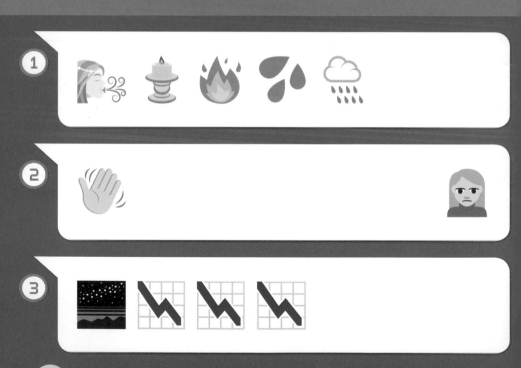

**1**

**2**

**3**

**4**

**5**

**6**

**7**

# Name the Song

......................................................

## ED SHEERAN

Rising to fame in 2013, and since then superstardom, Ed Sheeran is British music's most successful male export since John, Paul, Ringo and George. With more than 20 million albums sold and a bevvy of awards and honors for his songwriting, Ed is the champion of bedroom singer-songwriters who are now dominating the airwaves, YouTube, and streaming services. If you're looking for the voice of the future, you've found it. Here are some of his best songs in emoji. Can you work them out?

**1** 💯

**2**

**3**

**4**

**5**

**6**

**7**

# Name the Song

**THE BEATLES**

The Beatles have sold more than 600 million records since forming at the start of the sixties. They have no equals. John Lennon, Paul McCartney, George Harrison, and Ringo Starr had a chemistry so unique, so beloved, that their music changed the world. Without the Beatles, music as we know it simply wouldn't exist. And neither would emojis ...

**4**

**5**

**6**

**7**

# Name the Song

**BEST OF BOYBAND**

How many boybands can you name? There aren't as many around nowadays, but there was a time—the 1990s—when boybands were everywhere. And they were brilliant! From Boyz II Men to Backstreet Boys, Boyzone to Busted, boybands once ruled the airwaves and the hearts of teenage girls everywhere. So, put your bedazzled glittery costume on, get up from your stool, and sing these emoji puzzles loud and proud (and hopefully in tune)!

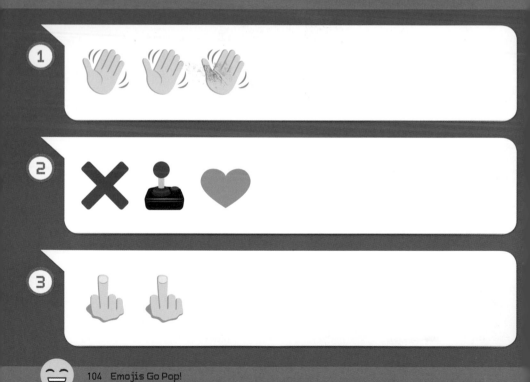

1.

2.

3.

**4**

**5**

**6**

**7**

# Name the Song

**BEYONCÉ**

As part of Destiny's Child in the late 90s and early 00s, it was clear that Beyoncé Knowles had all the charisma, personality, and determination necessary to run the world. Since then she has surpassed all expectations—today, she is irreplaceable. As a trivial tribute to her astonishing achievements, let's now salute this beautiful artist with seven fierce emoji puzzles.

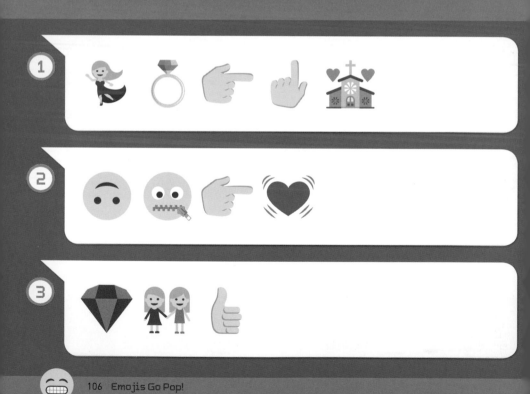

**4**       END

**5**

**6**

**7**

# Name the Song

**MICHAEL JACKSON**

Ever since he first strutted onto a dancefloor as part of the Jackson 5, Michael Jackson has remained the brightest star in the pop sky. His untimely death in 2009 robbed us of decades of new music. Even to his naysayers, Michael Jackson was the king of pop—to his millions of adoring fans, he was an icon whose music will live forever.

**1**

**2**

**3**

**4**

**5**

**6**

**7**

# Name the Song

**THE ROLLING STONES**

If the Beatles are beloved as the greatest band of all time, then the Rolling Stones are close runners-up. Formed in the early 1960s by founding members Mick Jagger, Keith Richards, Brian Jones, Bill Wyman, and Charlie Watts, the Rolling Stones have survived, outlived, and outperformed every other band from the 1960s, creating a huge legacy of excellent music. If you've ever wanted to see songs of the Stones in emoji form, then here you go!

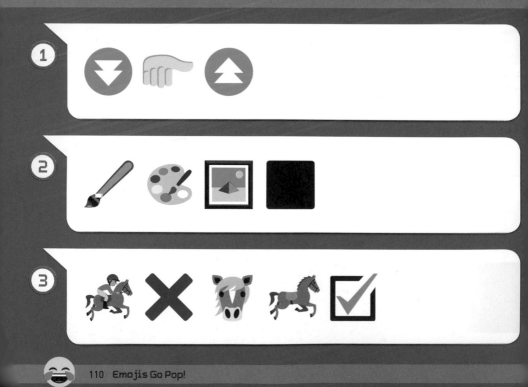

# Name the Song

.............................................................

**TAYLOR SWIFT**

Bursting on to the US country-music scene with her debut album in 2006, Tay Tay swiftly become the princess of pop. She wrote and performed her own tunes and was considered an authentic voice and a genuine talent. Fast forward to 2014, and her album *1989* become the all-singing, all-dancing pop masterpiece that has propelled her even further into superstardom. Nothing can stop her, so nothing should stop you—get solving these puzzles!

**4**

**5**

**6**

**7**

# Name the Song

**DRAKE**

Aubrey Drake Graham is more famous today than almost any other performer in the world, and is one of the most iconic celebrities to hit the stage since Michael Jackson. He is a prolific and intoxicating performer who knows no limits, as talented as he is swoon-worthy. His track "One Dance" was a global hit and he is the man that everyone wants to work with, be seen with, and be heard listening to. If you don't have a little Drake in your lives, then you're missing out!

**1**

**2**

**3**

**4**

**5**

**6**

**7**

# Name the Song

**BRITNEY SPEARS**

Ever since Ms Spears made her first appearance dressed as a schoolgirl in a music video, Britney has made men blush, women jealous, and gone on to become one of the most recognized singing voices on the planet. Her hits keep on coming and her songs are now as iconic as the once-famous pigtails. We have danced, kissed, and sung along to Britney's voice for almost two decades. We can't wait for the next two decades with her in our lives. Go Britney! Go Britney! Go Britney!

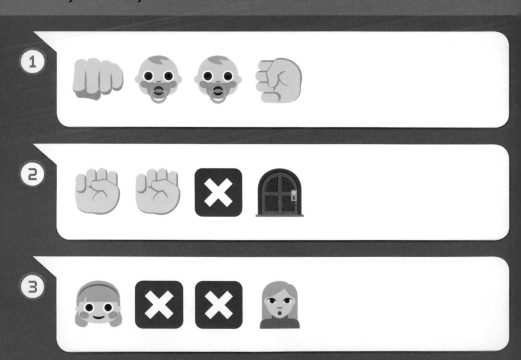

**4**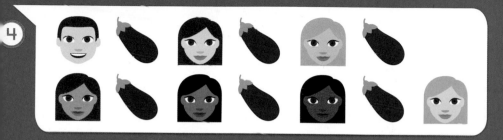

**5**

**6**

**7**

# Name the Song

**DON'T STOP THE POP!**

You know an instant classic when you hear one. The songs that enter your ears, get lost, and can never find their way out again. The following tunes are the very definition of classic pop hits that are so easy to sing and remember that they'll never be forgotten. Extra points are awarded if you can guess the song AND the artist who recorded it. We've thown in a few golden oldies, just in case the youngsters have begun to get too smug with their emoji-telligence.

**4**

**5**

**6**

**7**

# Name the Song

**CLASSIC POP**

Classic pop sounds so delicious that you always need a second helping. But this time we've gone a bit more obscure in our selection. You may need to ask your parents' help for some of these. We've rated these puzzles eleven on the emoji-meter, the highest it can go—if you can get these right, you're on your way to earning a gold star for good emoji-havior.

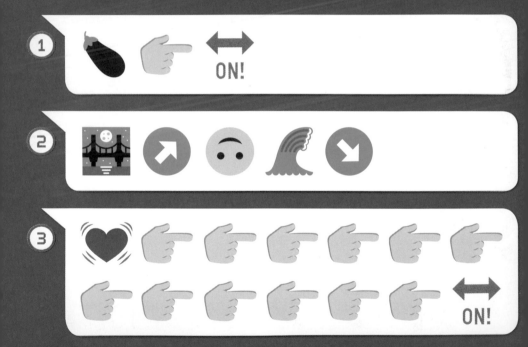

**4**

**5**

**6**

**7**

# Name the Song

## ROCK

Are you ready to rock? Are you ready to mosh? Are you ready to bang your head off? Good. Welcome to the rock zone. Things are about to get a little sweaty. Over the next few pages, we have compiled a selection of emoji puzzles for you rockers who like their emojis with long hair and a constant ringing in the ears. Get your devil horns at the ready and let's rock!

**4**

**5**

**6**

**7**

# Name the Song

## CLASSIC ROCK

Rock 'n' roll is up there with sliced bread as one of the greatest inventions conceived by humankind. And these songs are the bestest of the best, written by rock gods and handed down to us mere mortals as the soundtrack of our rebel souls. In honor of these gods, we've made these emoji puzzles a little bit more bone-quaking than the rest. Enjoy!

**1**

**2**

**3**

**4**

**5**

**6**

**7**

# Name the Song

............................................................

**DANCE**

As much as we like to rock and roll or jive and jiggle, it's also nice to twist and shout on the dancefloor, and that's where the following selection of emoji puzzles can be heard. This magic mix of dance tracks, classic and modern, is just the remedy for a long, hard week at work or school, when all you want to do is shake your blues away. A workout for your mind and body, don't stand still as you solve these puzzles—get on your feet and feel the rhythm!

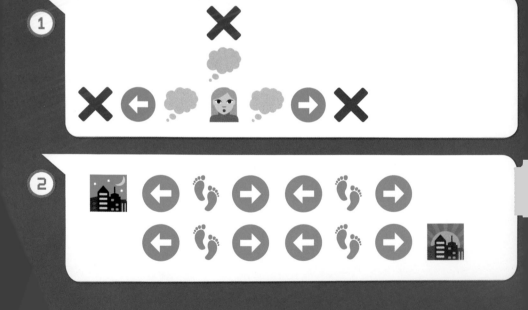

# Name the Song

**DAVID BOWIE**

In 2016 the world lost a global music icon: Mr. David Bowie. Since the 1960s, Bowie has been dancing in the street, living life on Mars and generally having a wonderful time soundtracking the rest of the world's lives. His millions of fans now celebrate the songwriter and performer as one of the greatest that ever lived. To honor his amazing musical legacy, let's salute him the best way we know how—with a devious emoji puzzle or two. These are for you Ziggy!

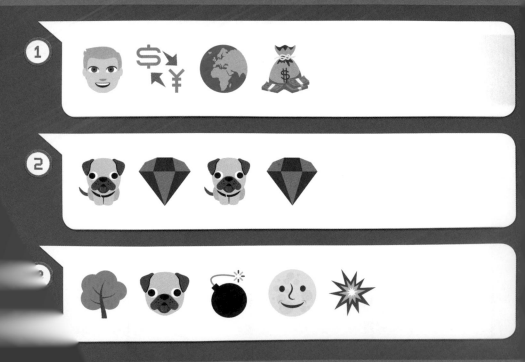

**4**

**5**

**7**

# Name the Song

**MADONNA**

Lady Madonna has been squeezing out hits for over 30 years, and she's been awesome at it since day one. In her illustrious career, Madge (as the Brits affectionately call her) has had more number-one hits than many other singing starlets, and has started and survived more musical trends than most. She is a world treasure, an icon of both stage, screen and song ... Madonna—take it away!

# Name the Band

**BAND NAMES**

The world is full of bands. Some of their names are bonkers. Some of them are brilliant. Some of them are just bad. But if you're going to release music that you want your fans to listen to, you need to have a name as catchy as your songs. The following selection of bands all have names that have become as famous as their music ... but who's your favorite?

**1**

**2**

**3**

**4**

**5**

**6**

# Name the Band

If you thought the previous page was too easy, then well done you. We've upped the difficulty level now—so get your thinking caps on. A selection of 90s rockers, 60s poppers and a few modern hitmakers round out this selection of puzzles. It's up to you to work out what goes where. Come on, keep up!

**4**

**5**

**6**

**7**

# Name the Album

## AGAINST THE CLOCK

For this random selection of album titles, let's up the ante a little. You've got 30 seconds to guess these titles. If you can't, you have to languish here in emoji-puzzle purgatory until you get them right. Should you get stuck on a certain puzzle, it's OK—these are rated nine on the emoji-meter.

**1**

**2**

**3**

**4**

**5**

**6**

**7**

# Pick 'n' Mix

Congratulations! You have reached our final page. You made it! And by the looks of things, only just! To celebrate sticking with us until the end, we have chosen a mix of all our main categories: movies, TV shows and music. All you have to do is guess which is which and then you can go for a nap. But, this being an emoji puzzle book, we've saved the hardest until last ... so good luck! And remember, everywhere you go, take an emoji with you!

**4**

**5**

**6**

**7**

# Answers

## Chapter 1: Let's All Go to the Movies!
•••••••••••••••

### 12–13 Name the Movie
ACTION
1. *Fast and Furious 8*
2. *Guardians of the Galaxy*
3. *King Arthur: Legend of the Sword*
4. *Kong: Skull Island*
5. *Bay Watch*
6. *Wonder Woman*
7. *Planet of the Apes*

### 14–15 Name the Movie
CLASSIC
1. *Singin' in the Rain*
2. *The Big Sleep*
3. *Psycho*
4. *Vertigo*
5. *Some Like It Hot*
6. *Breakfast at Tiffany's*
7. *E.T.*

### 16–17 Name the Movie
ACTION COMEDY
1. *Ghostbusters 2016*
2. *Pirates of the Caribbean: Dead Men Tell No Tales*
3. *Baby Driver*
4. *Spiderman: Homecoming*
5. *Kingsman 2: Golden Circle*
6. *Blade Runner 2049* (odd one out)
7. *Pacific Rim*

### 18–19 Name the Movie
BLOCKBUSTER
1. *Girl on the Train*
2. *Office Christmas Party*
3. *Sing!*
4. *Magnificent Seven*
5. *Titanic*
6. *Sausage Party*
7. *Interstellar*

### 20–21 Name the Movie
DISASTER
1. *Justice League*
2. *Thor*
3. *The Road*
4. *Independence Day*
5. *Deep Impact*
6. *Fifth Wave*
7. *The World's End*

### 22–23 Name the Movie
ANIMATED
1. *Cars 3*
2. *Kung Fu Panda 3*
3. *Zootopia*
4. *Ratatouille*
5. *The Emoji Movie*
6. *Paddington 2*
7. *The Jungle Book*

### 24–25 Name the Movie
SUPERHERO
1. *Logan*
2. *Captain America: Civil War*
3. *X-Men: Apocalypse*
4. *Ant Man*
5. *Superman*
6. *Robin Hood*
7. *Teenage Mutant Ninja Turtles*

### 26–27 Name the Movie
MONSTER
1. *Diary of a Wimpy Kid* (odd one out)
2. *Godzilla*
3. *Arachnophobia*
4. *The Devil Wears Prada*
5. *King Kong*
6. *Cloverfield*
7. *The Swarm*

### 28–29 Name the Movie
SPORT
1. *Raging Bull*
2. *Million Dollar Baby*
3. *Moneyball*
4. *Cool Hand Luke* (odd one out)
5. *The Basketball Diaries*
6. *Bend It Like Beckham*
7. *Dodgeball*

### 30–31 Name the Movie
CRIME
1. *Ghost in the Shell*
2. *Wolf of Wall Street*
3. *Silence of the Lambs*
4. *John Wick: Chapter Two*
5. *Murder on the Orient Express*
6. *Hateful Eight*
7. *Now You See Me 2*

### 32–33 Name the Movie
MASTERCLASS
1. *Taxi Driver*
2. *Gravity*
3. *Seven Samurai*
4. *Hell or High Water*
5. *Touch of Evil*
6. *Gone with the Wind*
7. *Moonlight*

### 34–35 Name the Movie
SEQUELS
1. *Matrix Revolutions*
2. *Trainspotting 2*
3. *Robocop 2*
4. *Scream 4*
5. *Bad Santa 2*
6. *Fistful of Dollars* (odd one out)
7. *Batman Returns*

**36–37 Name the Movie**
HORROR
1. *The Hills Have Eyes*
2. *Halloween 4*
3. *Let the Right One In*
4. *Cabin in the Woods*
5. *Zombieland*
6. *Lights Out*
7. *Split*

**38–39 Name the Movie**
ROMANTIC COMEDY
1. *The Wedding Singer*
2. *Never Been Kissed*
3. *Runaway Bride*
4. *Sixteen Candles*
5. *Gentleman Prefer Blondes*
6. *Romancing the Stone*
7. *Head over Heels*

**40–41 Name the Movie**
SCIENCE FICTION
1. *Mad Max Fury Road*
2. *A.I.*
3. *The Adjustment Bureau*
4. *Cowboys & Aliens*
5. *Cloud Atlas*
6. *Men in Black*
7. *Twelve Monkeys*

**42–43 Name the Movie**
FANTASY
1. *Alice in Wonderland*
2. *The Santa Clause*
3. *George's Dragon*
4. *Lord of the Rings: Return of the King*
5. *Freaky Friday*
6. *Monsters, Inc.*
7. *Chronicles of Narnia: The Lion, the Witch and the Wardrobe*

**44–45 Name the Movie**
MUSIC
1. *The Sound of Music*
2. *Dirty Dancing*
3. *Footloose*
4. *The Blues Brothers*
5. *The Bodyguard*
6. *24 Hour Party People*
7. *The Doors*

**46–47 Name the Movie**
THRILLER
1. *From Paris with Love*
2. *The Girl with the Dragon Tattoo*
3. *The A-Team* (odd one out)
4. *Seven*
5. *No Country for Old Men*
6. *The Accountant*
7. *Read My Lips*

**48–49 Name the Movie**
OSCAR WINNERS
1. *The Danish Girl*
2. *The Grand Budapest Hotel*
3. *The Imitation Game*
4. *Bridge of Spies*
5. *Boyhood*
6. *Midnight in Paris*
7. *The King's Speech*

**50–51 Name the Star**
BEST ACTOR
1. Brad Pitt (*The Curious Case of Benjamin Button*)
2. Daniel Day Lewis (*There Will Be Blood*)
3. George Clooney (*Men Who Stare at Goats*)
4. Heath Ledger/Jake Gyllenhaal (*Brokeback Mountain*)
5. Jamie Foxx (*Ray*)
6. Woody Allen (*Annie Hall*)
7. Chow Yun Fat (*Crouching Tiger, Hidden Dragon*)

**52–53 Name the Star**
BEST ACTRESS
1. Hilary Swank (*Girls Don't Cry*)
2. Sandra Bullock (*Speed*)
3. Kelly McGillis (*Top Gun*)
4. Julia Sawalha (*Chicken Run*)
5. Faye Dunaway (*Towering Inferno*)
6. Linda Blair (*The Exorcist*)
7. Sienna Miller (*American Sniper*)

**54–55 Name the Star**
BEST DIRECTOR
1. Stanley Kubrick (*A Clockwork Orange*)
2. Jonathan Demme (*Caged Heat*)
3. Jan de Bont (*Twister*)
4. Ridley Scott (*The Martian*)
5. Alfred Hitchcock (*Strangers on a Train*)
6. Alfred Hitchcock (*Dial M for Murder*)
7. Alexander Payne (*Sideways*)

# Chapter 2: Stars of the Small Screen
• • • • • • • • • • • • • •

**58–59 Name the Show**
BEST OF BINGEWATCH
1. *Bloodline*
2. *House of Cards*
3. *Wet Hot American Summer*
4. *13 Reasons Why*
5. *Stranger Things*
6. *Comedians in Cars Getting Coffee*
7. *Unbreakable Kimmy Schmidt*

**60–61 Name the Show**
COMEDY
1. *The Big Bang Theory*
2. *2 Broke Girls*
3. *Childrens Hospital*
4. *The Dukes Of Hazzard*
5. *Entourage*
6. *Family Guy*
7. *Home Improvement*

**62–63 Name the Show**
DRAMA
1. *Twin Peaks*

2. Orange Is the New Black
3. Agents of S.H.I.E.L.D.
4. American Horror Story
5. Hell on Wheels
6. Party of Five
7. Six Feet Under

**64–65 Name the Show**
EVEN MORE COMEDY
1. Blackadder Goes Forth
2. Community
3. Only Fools and Horses
4. The IT Crowd
5. The Golden Girls
6. Two and a Half Men
7. Family Ties

**66–67 Name the Show**
ACTION AND CRIME
1. Person of Interest
2. Knight Rider
3. Death in Paradise
4. Buffy the Vampire Slayer
5. The Flash
6. Star Trek
7. Lost

**68–69 Name the Show**
FANTASY AND REALITY
1. The Apprentice
2. Ice Road Truckers
3. The Crocodile Hunter
4. I'm a Celebrity... Get Me Out of Here!
5. Westworld
6. Being Human
7. The Walking Dead

**70–71 Name the Show**
SCIENCE FICTION
1. Invisible Man
2. The X-Files
3. Limitless
4. Doctor Who
5. Dragon Ball Z
6. Falling Skies
7. The Hitchiker's Guide to the Galaxy

**72–73 Name the Show**
ANIMATED
1. Robot Chicken
2. Scooby-Doo
3. Tom and Jerry
4. Inspector Gadget
5. Tweety & Sylvester
6. Thundercats
7. Winnie the Pooh

**74–75 Name the Show**
ROMANTIC DRAMA
1. Bones
2. Sex and the City
3. The Love Boat
4. Switched at Birth
5. Cheers
6. Chuck
7. I Dream of Jeannie

**76–77 Name the Show**
HEROES AND VILLAINS
1. Six Million Dollar Man
2. Bionic Woman
3. Thunderbirds
4. Dangermouse
5. Heroes
6. Bananaman
7. Power Rangers

**78–79 Name the Show**
EPIC DRAMA
1. The West Wing
2. Preacher
3. Prison Break
4. 24
5. Sons of Anarchy
6. Big Love
7. Friday Night Lights

**80–81 Name the Show**
BEST OF BRITISH
1. Upstairs, Downstairs
2. Top Gear
3. The Crown
4. The Great British Bake Off

5. The Night Manager
6. This Is England
7. Peep Show

**82–83 Name the Show**
BEST OF THE USA
1. Eastbound & Down
2. American Idol
3. The Bachelorette
4. Big Brother
5. Fresh Prince of Bel-Air
6. Happy Days
7. The Closer

**84–85 Name the Show**
A LITTLE BIT OF EVERYTHING
1. Sesame Street
2. Suits
3. Malcolm in the Middle
4. The Office
5. 30 Rock
6. Frasier
7. Game of Thrones

**86–87 Name the Show**
CLASSIC TV: UK
1. Dad's Army
2. Fawlty Towers
3. Weakest Link
4. The Jewel in the Crown
5. Last of the Summer Wine
6. A Touch of Frost
7. The Two Ronnies

**88–89 Name the Show**
CLASSIC TV: USA
1. Alf
2. Charlie's Angels
3. Chips
4. Doogie Howser, M.D.
5. Friends
6. Airwolf
7. Mister Ed

## 90—91 Random
*ANYTHING GOES*
1. *Planet Earth*
2. *Selfie*
3. *Shooter*
4. *The Last Man on Earth*
5. *The Odd Couple*
6. *Life on Mars*
7. *Friends with Benefits*

## 92—93 Random
*FILM AND SHOW*
1. *Transporter*
2. *Ace Ventura Pet Detective*
3. *Little Shop of Horrors*
4. *Taken*
5. *War of the Worlds*
6. *Tremors*
7. *Shaft*

# Chapter 3: Emojis Go Pop!

## 96—97 Name the Song
*POP*
1. "Party Monster"
2. "Eye Of The Tiger"
3. "Candle in the Wind"
4. "Love Is All Around"
5. "Three Lions"
6. "Last Christmas"
7. "Unchained Melody"

## 98—99 Name the Song
*ADELE*
1. "Set Fire to the Rain"
2. "Hello"
3. "Skyfall"
4. "Chasing Pavements"
5. "Water Under the Bridge"
6. "Crazy for You"
7. "Daydreamer"

## 100—101 Name the Song
*ED SHEERAN*
1. "Perfect"
2. "Castle on the Hill"
3. "Shape of You"
4. "Drunk"
5. "English Rose"
6. "I See Fire"
7. "Thinking Out Loud"

## 102—103 Name the Song
*THE BEATLES*
1. "Baby You're a Rich Man"
2. "Can'l Buy Me Love"
3. "Ticket to Ride"
4. "Fixing a Hole"
5. "Happiness is a Warm Gun"
6. "The Long and Winding Road"
7. "Twist and Shout"

## 104—105 Name the Song
*BEST OF BOYBAND*
1. "Bye Bye Bye"—NSYNC
2. "Quit Playing Games (With My Heart)"—Backstreet Boys
3. "Swear It Again"—Westlife
4. "Relight My Fire"—Take That
5. "End of the Road"—Boyz II Men
6. "I Want It That Way"—Backstreet Boys
7. "ABC"—Jackson 5

## 106—107 Name the Song
*BEYONCÉ*
1. "Single Ladies (Put A Ring On It)"
2. "Crazy in Love"
3. "Diamonds Are a Girl's Best Friend"
4. "End of Time"
5. "No Angel"
6. "Pray You Catch Me"
7. "Run The World (Girls)"

## 108—109 Name the Song
*MICHAEL JACKSON*
1. "Black or White"
2. "Earth Song"
3. "Man in the Mirror"
4. "Rockin' Robin"
5. "Speed Demon"
6. "Another Part of Me"
7. "Heal the World"

## 110—111 Name the Song
*THE ROLLING STONES*
1. "Under My Thumb"
2. "Paint It Black"
3. "Wild Horses"
4. "Sympathy for the Devil"
5. "Street Fightin' Man"
6. "She's a Rainbow"
7. "Get Off My Cloud"

## 112—113 Name the Song
*TAYLOR SWIFT*
1. "Shake It Off"
2. "Blank Space"
3. "Highway Don't Care"
4. "Fifteen"
5. "If This Was a Movie"
6. "Out of the Woods"
7. "Teardrops on My Guitar"

## 114—115 Name the Song
*DRAKE*
1. "Hotline Bling"
2. "Money to Blow"
3. "Champion"
4. "Diced Pineapples"
5. "Hate Sleeping Alone"
6. "Pop That"
7. "Round of Applause"

## 116—117 Name the Song
*BRITNEY SPEARS*
1. "Baby One More Time"
2. "Don't Go Knocking on My Door"
3. "I'm Not a Girl, Not Yet a Woman"
4. "Womanizer"
5. "Overprotected"
6. "Stronger"
7. "Toxic"

**118—119 Name the Song**
*DON'T STOP THE POP*
1. "I Just Called To Say I Love You"
2. "Over the Rainbow"
3. "Mr Blue Sky"
4. "Ain't No Sunshine"
5. "Big Yellow Taxi"
6. "Born to Run"
7. "Dancing Queen"

**120—121 Name the Song**
*CLASSIC POP*
1. "Let's Get It On"
2. "Bridge over Troubled Water"
3. "My Heart Will Go On"
4. "Livin' on a Prayer"
5. "Dancing in the Street"
6. "Hotel California"
7. "I Heard It Through the Grapevine"

**122—123 Name the Song**
*ROCK*
1. "Smells Like Teen Spirit"
2. "Enter Sandman"
3. "Rock Around the Clock"
4. "When Doves Cry"
5. "A Horse With No Name"
6. "Band on the Run"
7. "Riders on the Storm"

**124—125 Name the Song**
*CLASSIC ROCK*
1. "Walk This Way"
2. "Yesterday"
3. "Black Hole Sun"
4. "Strawberry Fields Forever"
5. "Basket Case"
6. "Smoke on the Water"
7. "Welcome to the Jungle"

**126—127 Name the Song**
*DANCE*
1. "Can't Get You out of My Head"
2. "Twistin' the Night Away"
3. "Wake Me Up Before You Go-Go"
4. "Re-Rewind (The Crowd Say Bo Selecta)"
5. "Love Shack"
6. "Seven Nation Army"
7. "Jump Around"

**128—129 Name the Song**
*DAVID BOWIE*
1. "The Man Who Sold the World"
2. "Diamond Dogs"
3. "Fall Dog Bombs the Moon"
4. "Friday on My Mind"
5. "Hallo Spaceboy"
6. "Let's Spend the Night Together"
7. "Space Oddity"

**130—131 Name the Song**
*MADONNA*
1. "Like a Virgin"
2. "Don't Cry For Me Argentina"
3. "Dress You Up"
4. "Frozen"
5. "Lucky Star"
6. "Material Girl"
7. "Borderline"

**132—133 Name the Band**
*BAND NAMES*
1. One Direction
2. Coldplay
3. Radiohead
4. 3 Doors Down
5. Abba
6. Arcade Fire
7. Red Hot Chili Peppers

**134—135 Name the Band**
*MORE CHALLENGING BAND NAMES*
1. The Beautiful South
2. Dire Straits
3. Oasis
4. Blur
5. Arctic Monkeys
6. Amy Winehouse
7. The Flaming Lips

**136—137 Name the Album**
*AGAINST THE CLOCK*
1. 24K Magic
2. Views
3. Lemonade
4. A Head Full of Dreams
5. Pet Sounds
6. Chocolate Starfish and the Hot Dog Flavored Water
7. Beauty Behind the Madness

**138—139 Pic 'n' Mix**
1. *Mary Poppins*
2. *One Flew Over the Cuckoo's Nest*
3. *Fight Club*
4. "Three Times a Lady"
5. "Cloud Nine"
6. *21 Jump Street*
7. *Lost in Space*

Emoji artwork supplied by Emoji One (http://emojione.com)